**W9-CXZ-730**

At the end of the school day, the Breakfast Bunch pack up their things.

Dee, I don't know why you care so much about the Read-a-thon.

Yeah, especially with the new X-Station 5000 game system coming out in a few days!

Hector, everyone's life doesn't revolve around electronics.

C'mon, we're stopping by the school library.

I'll get my camera.

I'll get my audio recorder.

They're corrupting our children!

Rotting their minds!

And enrollment in the Read-a-thon is at an all-time low!

Who is that?

Vivian Bookwormer, the public librarian.

Well, Vivian, looks like it's time for a little divide and conquer.

Betty, I'm going undercover!

Later . . .

PUBLIC LIBRARY

Betty, do you read me?

Spork Phone

Loud and clear!

I'm going in!

TAP TAP TAP

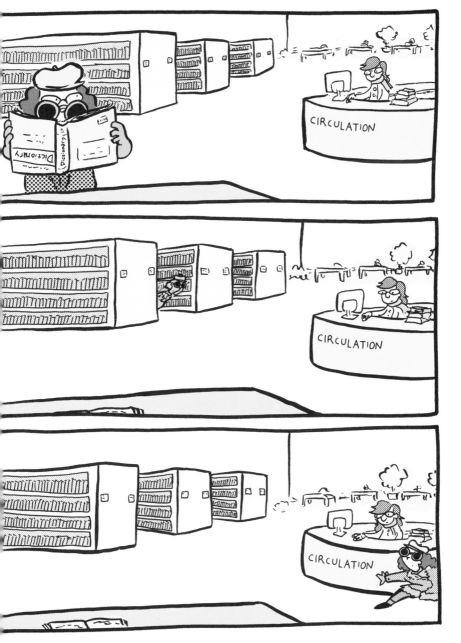

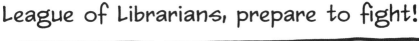

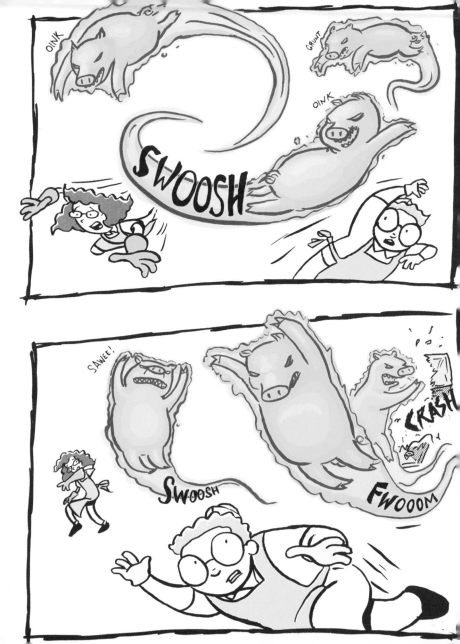

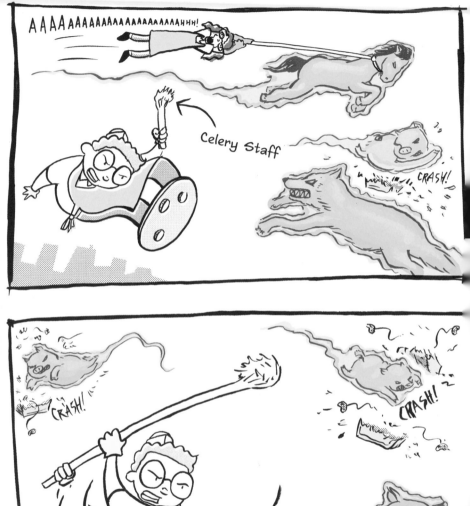

Sonic-Boom
Juice Box

BOOM!

Hairnet Nets

Lunch Lady, combining the Read-a-thon with a chance to play the new X-Station 5000 was a great idea! Thanks again for filling in after I told you that the librarians had been arrested.
Well, thank you, Principal Hernandez. "Read while you wait to play" is the rule!
READ
READ-A-THON
ZOOP
ZAP

# For Mrs. Krosoczka and Ralph Macchio
## –J.J.K.

THIS IS A BORZOI BOOK PUBLISHED BY ALFRED A. KNOPF

All rights reserved. Published in the United States by Alfred A. Knopf, an imprint of Random House Children's Books, a division of Random House, Inc., New York.

Knopf, Borzoi Books, and the colophon are registered trademarks of Random House, Inc.

Visit us on the Web! www.randomhouse.com/kids

Educators and librarians, for a variety of teaching tools,
visit us at www.randomhouse.com/teachers

*Library of Congress Cataloging-in-Publication Data*
Krosoczka, Jarrett.
Lunch Lady and the League of Librarians / Jarrett J. Krosoczka. — 1st ed.
p. cm.
Summary: The school lunch lady, a secret crime fighter, sets out to stop a group
of librarians bent on destroying a shipment of video games while a group of students
known as the Breakfast Bunch provides backup.
ISBN 978-0-375-84684-7 (trade pbk.) — ISBN 978-0-375-94684-4 (lib. bdg.)
1. Graphic novels. [1. Graphic novels. 2. Librarians—Fiction. 3. Books and reading—Fiction.
4. School lunchrooms, cafeterias, etc.—Fiction. 5. Schools—Fiction.] I. Title.
PZ7.7.K76Lul 2009     [Fic]—dc22     2008043117

The text of this book is set in 11-point Hedge Backwards Lower.

MANUFACTURED IN MALAYSIA
July 2009
20 19 18 17 16 15 14 13 12 11

First Edition